THE

FAMILY

RECORD

a workbook

**Devised by
Henry J. Craig**

Copyright 2010 Aberdeen & North-East Scotland Family History Society

(www.anesfhs.org.uk)

ISBN: 0-947659-91-9
978-0-947659-91-2

First published November 1988

Reprinted 1990, 1991, 1992, 1993,1994,
1996, 1997, 1998, 2001, 2003, 2004,
2005, 2006, 2007, 2008 (twice), 2009 (3 times)

ISBN: 978-1-905004-20-1

Second Edition

First published 2010
Reprinted 2011, 2012 (twice)
Reprinted 2014 (twice)

Published by
Aberdeen & North-East Scotland Family History Society

Printed by
McKenzie Quality Print Ltd.,Unit 12, Wellheads Crescent, Dyce, Aberdeen AB21 7GA

THE FAMILY RECORD

This system was devised by Mr Henry Craig of Inverurie. He needed some way of keeping those records and this system was born. Having contacted us on other matters he then presented these to the Society to do with as they wished. Our grateful and heartfelt thanks go to Mr Craig who has now been given life membership of the Aberdeen & North East Scotland Family History Society.

The Society was quick to see the potential of the System and we are pleased to offer it to you in the hope it might solve the problem of record keeping. A lot of members have contacted us with a request for a book of some kind to keep their information in and we hope this will answer all their needs.

In view of the increasing amount of information that is becoming available we have now added space for Census details plus a Contents and Certificates page.

With this small illustration I hope you will see how it works.

From the centre page to the front is your father's family and from the centre to the back is your mother's.

Each entry on the centre page is numbered and the corresponding page holds all the information about that person.

NAME	George Muggins
Born	13 April 1830
Address	17 Greenacre Road
	Aberdeen
Parents	(Page ?)
Father	Joseph Muggins
Mother	Christian M.S. Whatsername
Married	24 Dec. 1824 Parish St Clements
Died	27 Aug. 1913 Age 83
Address	108 North Road
	Aberdeen
Buried	St Clements

Census Address	
1841	108 North Rd, Aberdeen
1851	108 North Rd, Aberdeen
1861	108 North Rd, Aberdeen
1871	108 North Rd, Aberdeen
1881	108 North Rd, Aberdeen
1891	108 North Rd, Aberdeen
1901	108 North Rd, Aberdeen
1911	108 North Rd, Aberdeen

NAME	Anne Other
Born	7 May 1833
Address	Weavers Croft
	Potgreen Belhelvie
Parents	(Page ?)
Father	William Other
Mother	Barbara M.S. Thingamy
Married	10 Oct. 1830 Parish Belhelvie
Died	15 Nov. 1909 Age 76
Address	108 North Road
	Aberdeen
Buried	St Clements

Census Address	
1841	Weavers Croft, Potgreen
1851	Weavers Croft, Potgreen
1861	108 North Rd, Aberdeen
1871	108 North Rd, Aberdeen
1881	108 North Rd, Aberdeen
1891	108 North Rd, Aberdeen
1901	108 North Rd, Aberdeen
1911	

Married	25 Sept. 1855	Address	Potgreen, Belhelvie	
Name	George Muggins	Age	25 Occupation	Lax Fisher
Address	108 North Road, Aberdeen			
Father Alive or Deceased	Alive	Mother Alive or Deceased		Alive
Name	Anne Other	Age	23 Occupation	Seamstress
Address	Weavers Croft, Potgreen, Belhelvie			
Father Alive or Deceased	Alive	Mother Alive or Deceased		Deceased
Witnesses	William Muggins (Brother)		John Other (Uncle)	

FAMILY			
NAME	DATE	ADDRESS	FURTHER INFO
Joseph	1 July 1856	108 North Rd. Aberdeen	Drowned at Sea Nov. 1885
Barbara	17 Aug 1858	108 North Rd. Aberdeen	Died young Mar 1859
Christian	29 June 1859	21 West St. Belhelvie	mar. John Whatsit Jan 1882
William	29 June 1859	5 Main Rd. Turriff	mar. Jannet Orre June 1883
George	6 May 1861	Church Close, Fyvie	mar. Ann Whoseit Sept 1885
Anne	13 June 1862	108 North Rd. Aberdeen	d. unmarried Mar 1922
John	24 Mar 1863		Emigrated New York Apr 1881
		108 North Road Aberdeen	Passd to eldest son of
			William & Jannet Orre
			named George in May 1922

NAME

Born	
Address	

Parents (Page)
Father
Mother   M.S.
Married   Parish

Died _____ Age _____
Address

Buried

Census Address	
1841	
1851	
1861	
1871	
1881	
1891	
1901	
1911	

NAME

Born	
Address	

Parents (Page)
Father
Mother   M.S.
Married   Parish

Died _____ Age _____
Address

Buried

Census Address	
1841	
1851	
1861	
1871	
1881	
1891	
1901	
1911	

Married   Address

Name _____ Age _____ Occupation _____
Address
Father Alive or Deceased   Mother Alive or Deceased
Name _____ Age _____ Occupation _____
Address
Father Alive or Deceased   Mother Alive or Deceased
Witnesses

FAMILY			
NAME	DATE	ADDRESS	FURTHER INFO

NAME		NAME	
Born		Born	
Address		Address	
Parents (Page)		Parents (Page)	
Father		Father	
Mother	M.S.	Mother	M.S.
Married	Parish	Married	Parish
Died	Age	Died	Age
Address		Address	
Buried		Buried	

Census Address		Census Address	
1841		1841	
1851		1851	
1861		1861	
1871		1871	
1881		1881	
1891		1891	
1901		1901	
1911		1911	

Married   Address

Name	Age	Occupation
Address		
Father Alive or Deceased	Mother Alive or Deceased	
Name	Age	Occupation
Address		
Father Alive or Deceased	Mother Alive or Deceased	
Witnesses		

FAMILY			
NAME	DATE	ADDRESS	FURTHER INFO

NAME

| Born | |
| Address | |

Parents   (Page)
Father
Mother   M.S.
Married   Parish

| Died | _____Age _____ |
| Address | |

Buried

Census Address	
1841	
1851	
1861	
1871	
1881	
1891	
1901	
1911	

NAME

| Born | |
| Address | |

Parents   (Page)
Father
Mother   M.S.
Married   Parish

| Died | _____Age _____ |
| Address | |

Buried

Census Address	
1841	
1851	
1861	
1871	
1881	
1891	
1901	
1911	

Married   Address

Name	Age _____ Occupation
Address	
Father Alive or Deceased	Mother Alive or Deceased
Name	Age _____ Occupation
Address	
Father Alive or Deceased	Mother Alive or Deceased
Witnesses	

FAMILY			
NAME	DATE	ADDRESS	FURTHER INFO

NAME

| Born | |
| Address | |

Parents (Page)	
Father	
Mother	M.S.
Married	Parish

Died	Age
Address	
Buried	

Census Address	
1841	
1851	
1861	
1871	
1881	
1891	
1901	
1911	

NAME

| Born | |
| Address | |

Parents (Page)	
Father	
Mother	M.S.
Married	Parish

Died	Age
Address	
Buried	

Census Address	
1841	
1851	
1861	
1871	
1881	
1891	
1901	
1911	

Married   Address

Name	Age	Occupation
Address		
Father Alive or Deceased	Mother Alive or Deceased	
Name	Age	Occupation
Address		
Father Alive or Deceased	Mother Alive or Deceased	
Witnesses		

FAMILY			
NAME	DATE	ADDRESS	FURTHER INFO

NAME

Born	_____
Address	_____

Parents (Page)	_____
Father	_____
Mother	M.S.
Married	Parish

Died	_____Age _____
Address	_____
	_____
Buried	

Census Address	
1841	
1851	
1861	
1871	
1881	
1891	
1901	
1911	

NAME

Born	_____
Address	_____

Parents (Page)	_____
Father	_____
Mother	M.S.
Married	Parish

Died	_____Age _____
Address	_____
	_____
Buried	

Census Address	
1841	
1851	
1861	
1871	
1881	
1891	
1901	
1911	

Married _____ Address _____

Name	_____ Age _____ Occupation _____
Address	_____
Father Alive or Deceased	Mother Alive or Deceased
Name	_____ Age _____ Occupation _____
Address	_____
Father Alive or Deceased	Mother Alive or Deceased
Witnesses	

FAMILY			
NAME	DATE	ADDRESS	FURTHER INFO

NAME		NAME	
Born		Born	
Address		Address	
Parents (Page)		Parents (Page)	
Father		Father	
Mother	M.S.	Mother	M.S.
Married	Parish	Married	Parish
Died	Age	Died	Age
Address		Address	
Buried		Buried	

Census Address		Census Address	
1841		1841	
1851		1851	
1861		1861	
1871		1871	
1881		1881	
1891		1891	
1901		1901	
1911		1911	

Married   Address

Name	Age	Occupation
Address		
Father Alive or Deceased	Mother Alive or Deceased	
Name	Age	Occupation
Address		
Father Alive or Deceased	Mother Alive or Deceased	
Witnesses		

FAMILY			
NAME	DATE	ADDRESS	FURTHER INFO

NAME

Born	
Address	
Parents (Page)	
Father	
Mother	M.S.
Married	Parish
Died	Age
Address	
Buried	

Census Address	
1841	
1851	
1861	
1871	
1881	
1891	
1901	
1911	

NAME

Born	
Address	
Parents (Page)	
Father	
Mother	M.S.
Married	Parish
Died	Age
Address	
Buried	

Census Address	
1841	
1851	
1861	
1871	
1881	
1891	
1901	
1911	

Married   Address

Name	Age Occupation
Address	
Father Alive or Deceased	Mother Alive or Deceased
Name	Age Occupation
Address	
Father Alive or Deceased	Mother Alive or Deceased
Witnesses	

FAMILY			
NAME	DATE	ADDRESS	FURTHER INFO

NAME

Born	
Address	
Parents (Page)	
Father	
Mother	M.S.
Married	Parish
Died	Age
Address	
Buried	

Census Address	
1841	
1851	
1861	
1871	
1881	
1891	
1901	
1911	

NAME

Born	
Address	
Parents (Page)	
Father	
Mother	M.S.
Married	Parish
Died	Age
Address	
Buried	

Census Address	
1841	
1851	
1861	
1871	
1881	
1891	
1901	
1911	

Married   Address

Name	Age	Occupation
Address		
Father Alive or Deceased	Mother Alive or Deceased	
Name	Age	Occupation
Address		
Father Alive or Deceased	Mother Alive or Deceased	
Witnesses		

FAMILY			
NAME	DATE	ADDRESS	FURTHER INFO

NAME

Born	_____
Address	_____
	_____

Parents (Page 1)	_____
Father	_____
Mother	_____ M.S.
Married	Parish

Died	_____ Age ____
Address	_____
	_____
Buried	

NAME

Born	_____
Address	_____
	_____

Parents (Page 2)	_____
Father	_____
Mother	_____ M.S.
Married	Parish

Died	_____ Age ____
Address	_____
	_____
Buried	

Census Address
1841
1851
1861
1871
1881
1891
1901
1911

Census Address
1841
1851
1861
1871
1881
1891
1901
1911

Married   Address

Name	_____ Age ____ Occupation _____
Address	_____
Father Alive or Deceased	Mother Alive or Deceased
Name	_____ Age ____ Occupation _____
Address	_____
Father Alive or Deceased	Mother Alive or Deceased
Witnesses	

FAMILY			
NAME	DATE	ADDRESS	FURTHER INFO

NAME _____

Born _____
Address _____
_____

Parents (Page 3) _____
Father _____
Mother _____ M.S. _____
Married _____ Parish _____
Died _____ Age _____
Address _____
_____
_____
Buried _____

Census Address	
1841	
1851	
1861	
1871	
1881	
1891	
1901	
1911	

NAME _____

Born _____
Address _____
_____

Parents (Page 4) _____
Father _____
Mother _____ M.S. _____
Married _____ Parish _____
Died _____ Age _____
Address _____
_____
_____
Buried _____

Census Address	
1841	
1851	
1861	
1871	
1881	
1891	
1901	
1911	

Married _____ Address _____

Name _____ Age _____ Occupation _____
Address _____
Father Alive or Deceased _____ Mother Alive or Deceased _____
Name _____ Age _____ Occupation _____
Address _____
Father Alive or Deceased _____ Mother Alive or Deceased _____
Witnesses _____

FAMILY			
NAME	DATE	ADDRESS	FURTHER INFO

NAME

Born	
Address	
Parents	(Page 5)
Father	
Mother	M.S.
Married	Parish
Died	Age
Address	
Buried	

Census Address	
1841	
1851	
1861	
1871	
1881	
1891	
1901	
1911	

NAME

Born	
Address	
Parents	(Page 6)
Father	
Mother	M.S.
Married	Parish
Died	Age
Address	
Buried	

Census Address	
1841	
1851	
1861	
1871	
1881	
1891	
1901	
1911	

Married   Address

Name	Age	Occupation
Address		
Father Alive or Deceased	Mother Alive or Deceased	
Name	Age	Occupation
Address		
Father Alive or Deceased	Mother Alive or Deceased	
Witnesses		

FAMILY			
NAME	DATE	ADDRESS	FURTHER INFO

NAME _____

Born	_____
Address	_____
	_____
Parents (Page 7)	_____
Father	_____
Mother	_____ M.S.
Married	Parish
Died	_____ Age _____
Address	_____
	_____
Buried	_____

NAME _____

Born	_____
Address	_____
	_____
Parents (Page 8)	_____
Father	_____
Mother	_____ M.S.
Married	Parish
Died	_____ Age _____
Address	_____
	_____
Buried	_____

Census Address	
1841	
1851	
1861	
1871	
1881	
1891	
1901	
1911	

Census Address	
1841	
1851	
1861	
1871	
1881	
1891	
1901	
1911	

Married _____ Address _____

Name	_____ Age _____ Occupation _____
Address	_____
Father Alive or Deceased	Mother Alive or Deceased
Name	_____ Age _____ Occupation _____
Address	_____
Father Alive or Deceased	Mother Alive or Deceased
Witnesses	

FAMILY			
NAME	DATE	ADDRESS	FURTHER INFO

NAME

Born	_____
Address	_____
	_____
Parents (Page 9)	_____
Father	_____
Mother	_____ M.S.
Married	Parish
Died	_____ Age ____
Address	_____
	_____
Buried	

NAME

Born	_____
Address	_____
	_____
Parents (Page 10)	_____
Father	_____
Mother	_____ M.S.
Married	Parish
Died	_____ Age ____
Address	_____
	_____
Buried	

Census Address
1841
1851
1861
1871
1881
1891
1901
1911

Census Address
1841
1851
1861
1871
1881
1891
1901
1911

Married   Address

Name _____	Age _____ Occupation _____
Address _____	
Father Alive or Deceased	Mother Alive or Deceased
Name _____	Age _____ Occupation _____
Address _____	
Father Alive or Deceased	Mother Alive or Deceased
Witnesses	

FAMILY			
NAME	DATE	ADDRESS	FURTHER INFO

NAME

| Born | |
| Address | |

Parents (Page 11)
Father
Mother   M.S.
Married   Parish

| Died | Age |
| Address | |

Buried

Census Address	
1841	
1851	
1861	
1871	
1881	
1891	
1901	
1911	

NAME

| Born | |
| Address | |

Parents (Page 12)
Father
Mother   M.S.
Married   Parish

| Died | Age |
| Address | |

Buried

Census Address	
1841	
1851	
1861	
1871	
1881	
1891	
1901	
1911	

Married   Address

Name	Age	Occupation
Address		
Father Alive or Deceased	Mother Alive or Deceased	
Name	Age	Occupation
Address		
Father Alive or Deceased	Mother Alive or Deceased	
Witnesses		

FAMILY			
NAME	DATE	ADDRESS	FURTHER INFO

NAME

Born	
Address	
Parents (Page 13)	
Father	
Mother	M.S.
Married	Parish
Died	Age
Address	
Buried	

NAME

Born	
Address	
Parents (Page 14)	
Father	
Mother	M.S.
Married	Parish
Died	Age
Address	
Buried	

Census Address	
1841	
1851	
1861	
1871	
1881	
1891	
1901	
1911	

Census Address	
1841	
1851	
1861	
1871	
1881	
1891	
1901	
1911	

Married   Address

Name	Age _____ Occupation
Address	
Father Alive or Deceased	Mother Alive or Deceased
Name	Age _____ Occupation
Address	
Father Alive or Deceased	Mother Alive or Deceased
Witnesses	

FAMILY			
NAME	DATE	ADDRESS	FURTHER INFO

NAME

Born	
Address	

Parents (Page 15)	
Father	
Mother	M.S.
Married	Parish

Died	Age
Address	
Buried	

Census Address	
1841	
1851	
1861	
1871	
1881	
1891	
1901	
1911	

NAME

Born	
Address	

Parents (Page 17)	
Father	
Mother	M.S.
Married	Parish

Died	Age
Address	
Buried	

Census Address	
1841	
1851	
1861	
1871	
1881	
1891	
1901	
1911	

Married   Address

Name	Age	Occupation
Address		
Father Alive or Deceased	Mother Alive or Deceased	
Name	Age	Occupation
Address		
Father Alive or Deceased	Mother Alive or Deceased	
Witnesses		

FAMILY			
NAME	DATE	ADDRESS	FURTHER INFO

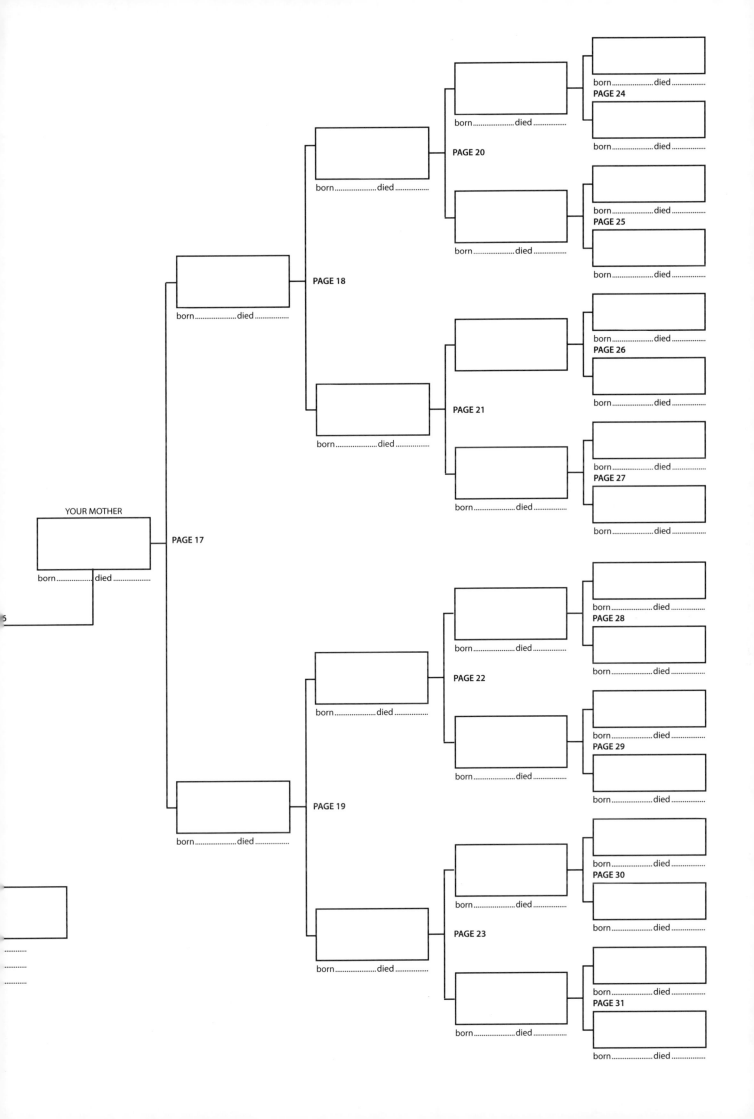

YOUR MOTHER

born.................died..................

PAGE 17

PAGE 18

born.................died..................

PAGE 19

born.................died..................

PAGE 20

born.................died..................

PAGE 21

born.................died..................

PAGE 22

born.................died..................

PAGE 23

born.................died..................

PAGE 24

born.................died..................

born.................died..................

PAGE 25

born.................died..................

born.................died..................

PAGE 26

born.................died..................

born.................died..................

PAGE 27

born.................died..................

born.................died..................

PAGE 28

born.................died..................

born.................died..................

PAGE 29

born.................died..................

born.................died..................

PAGE 30

born.................died..................

born.................died..................

PAGE 31

born.................died..................

born.................died..................

NAME

Born	
Address	

Parents (Page 18)	
Father	
Mother	M.S.
Married	Parish

Died	Age
Address	
Buried	

Census Address	
1841	
1851	
1861	
1871	
1881	
1891	
1901	
1911	

NAME

Born	
Address	

Parents (Page 19)	
Father	
Mother	M.S.
Married	Parish

Died	Age
Address	
Buried	

Census Address	
1841	
1851	
1861	
1871	
1881	
1891	
1901	
1911	

Married		Address	
Name		Age	Occupation
Address			
Father Alive or Deceased		Mother Alive or Deceased	
Name		Age	Occupation
Address			
Father Alive or Deceased		Mother Alive or Deceased	
Witnesses			

FAMILY			
NAME	DATE	ADDRESS	FURTHER INFO

NAME

Born	
Address	
Parents (Page 20)	
Father	
Mother	M.S.
Married	Parish
Died	Age
Address	
Buried	

Census Address	
1841	
1851	
1861	
1871	
1881	
1891	
1901	
1911	

NAME

Born	
Address	
Parents (Page 21)	
Father	
Mother	M.S.
Married	Parish
Died	Age
Address	
Buried	

Census Address	
1841	
1851	
1861	
1871	
1881	
1891	
1901	
1911	

Married   Address

Name	Age Occupation
Address	
Father Alive or Deceased	Mother Alive or Deceased
Name	Age Occupation
Address	
Father Alive or Deceased	Mother Alive or Deceased
Witnesses	

FAMILY			
NAME	DATE	ADDRESS	FURTHER INFO

NAME

Born	_____
Address	_____
Parents (Page 22)	_____
Father	_____
Mother	M.S.
Married	Parish
Died	_____Age _____
Address	_____
	_____
Buried	

NAME

Born	_____
Address	_____
Parents (Page 23)	_____
Father	_____
Mother	M.S.
Married	Parish
Died	_____Age _____
Address	_____
	_____
Buried	

Census Address
1841
1851
1861
1871
1881
1891
1901
1911

Census Address
1841
1851
1861
1871
1881
1891
1901
1911

Married   Address

Name _____	Age _____ Occupation _____
Address _____	
Father Alive or Deceased	Mother Alive or Deceased
Name _____	Age _____ Occupation _____
Address _____	
Father Alive or Deceased	Mother Alive or Deceased
Witnesses	

FAMILY			
NAME	DATE	ADDRESS	FURTHER INFO

NAME

Born _____

Address _____

_____

Parents (Page 24) _____

Father _____

Mother _____ M.S.

Married _____ Parish

Died _____ Age _____

Address _____

_____

Buried

Census Address	
1841	
1851	
1861	
1871	
1881	
1891	
1901	
1911	

NAME

Born _____

Address _____

_____

Parents (Page 25) _____

Father _____

Mother _____ M.S.

Married _____ Parish

Died _____ Age _____

Address _____

_____

Buried

Census Address	
1841	
1851	
1861	
1871	
1881	
1891	
1901	
1911	

Married _____ Address _____

Name _____ Age _____ Occupation _____

Address _____

Father Alive or Deceased _____ Mother Alive or Deceased _____

Name _____ Age _____ Occupation _____

Address _____

Father Alive or Deceased _____ Mother Alive or Deceased _____

Witnesses

FAMILY			
NAME	DATE	ADDRESS	FURTHER INFO

NAME

Born	
Address	
Parents (Page 26)	
Father	
Mother	M.S.
Married	Parish
Died	Age
Address	
Buried	

Census Address	
1841	
1851	
1861	
1871	
1881	
1891	
1901	
1911	

NAME

Born	
Address	
Parents (Page 27)	
Father	
Mother	M.S.
Married	Parish
Died	Age
Address	
Buried	

Census Address	
1841	
1851	
1861	
1871	
1881	
1891	
1901	
1911	

Married   Address

Name	Age	Occupation
Address		
Father Alive or Deceased	Mother Alive or Deceased	
Name	Age	Occupation
Address		
Father Alive or Deceased	Mother Alive or Deceased	
Witnesses		

FAMILY			
NAME	DATE	ADDRESS	FURTHER INFO

NAME

Born
Address

Parents   (Page 28)
Father
Mother   M.S.
Married   Parish
Died _____Age _____
Address

Buried

NAME

Born
Address

Parents   (Page 29)
Father
Mother   M.S.
Married   Parish
Died _____Age _____
Address

Buried

Census Address
1841
1851
1861
1871
1881
1891
1901
1911

Census Address
1841
1851
1861
1871
1881
1891
1901
1911

Married   Address

Name	Age _____ Occupation
Address	
Father Alive or Deceased	Mother Alive or Deceased
Name	Age _____ Occupation
Address	
Father Alive or Deceased	Mother Alive or Deceased
Witnesses	

FAMILY			
NAME	DATE	ADDRESS	FURTHER INFO

NAME		NAME	
Born		Born	
Address		Address	
Parents (Page 30)		Parents (Page 31)	
Father		Father	
Mother	M.S.	Mother	M.S.
Married	Parish	Married	Parish
Died	Age	Died	Age
Address		Address	
Buried		Buried	

Census Address		Census Address	
1841		1841	
1851		1851	
1861		1861	
1871		1871	
1881		1881	
1891		1891	
1901		1901	
1911		1911	

Married   Address

Name	Age	Occupation
Address		
Father Alive or Deceased	Mother Alive or Deceased	
Name	Age	Occupation
Address		
Father Alive or Deceased	Mother Alive or Deceased	
Witnesses		

FAMILY			
NAME	DATE	ADDRESS	FURTHER INFO

NAME

Born

Address

Parents (Page)

Father

Mother   M.S.

Married   Parish

Died _____ Age _____

Address

Buried

Census Address	
1841	
1851	
1861	
1871	
1881	
1891	
1901	
1911	

NAME

Born

Address

Parents (Page)

Father

Mother   M.S.

Married   Parish

Died _____ Age _____

Address

Buried

Census Address	
1841	
1851	
1861	
1871	
1881	
1891	
1901	
1911	

Married   Address

Name _____ Age _____ Occupation _____

Address

Father Alive or Deceased   Mother Alive or Deceased

Name _____ Age _____ Occupation _____

Address

Father Alive or Deceased   Mother Alive or Deceased

Witnesses

FAMILY			
NAME	DATE	ADDRESS	FURTHER INFO

NAME

Born	
Address	

Parents　(Page)
Father	
Mother	M.S.
Married	Parish

Died	Age
Address	
Buried	

Census Address	
1841	
1851	
1861	
1871	
1881	
1891	
1901	
1911	

NAME

Born	
Address	

Parents　(Page)
Father	
Mother	M.S.
Married	Parish

Died	Age
Address	
Buried	

Census Address	
1841	
1851	
1861	
1871	
1881	
1891	
1901	
1911	

Married　　　　　　　　　　　　　Address

Name	Age	Occupation
Address		
Father Alive or Deceased	Mother Alive or Deceased	
Name	Age	Occupation
Address		
Father Alive or Deceased	Mother Alive or Deceased	
Witnesses		

FAMILY			
NAME	DATE	ADDRESS	FURTHER INFO

NAME		NAME	
Born		Born	
Address		Address	
Parents (Page)		Parents (Page)	
Father		Father	
Mother	M.S.	Mother	M.S.
Married	Parish	Married	Parish
Died	Age	Died	Age
Address		Address	
Buried		Buried	

Census Address		Census Address	
1841		1841	
1851		1851	
1861		1861	
1871		1871	
1881		1881	
1891		1891	
1901		1901	
1911		1911	

Married   Address

Name	Age	Occupation
Address		
Father Alive or Deceased	Mother Alive or Deceased	
Name	Age	Occupation
Address		
Father Alive or Deceased	Mother Alive or Deceased	
Witnesses		

FAMILY			
NAME	DATE	ADDRESS	FURTHER INFO

NAME

Born	
Address	
Parents (Page)	
Father	
Mother	M.S.
Married	Parish
Died	Age
Address	
Buried	

Census Address	
1841	
1851	
1861	
1871	
1881	
1891	
1901	
1911	

NAME

Born	
Address	
Parents (Page)	
Father	
Mother	M.S.
Married	Parish
Died	Age
Address	
Buried	

Census Address	
1841	
1851	
1861	
1871	
1881	
1891	
1901	
1911	

Married   Address

Name		Age	Occupation
Address			
Father Alive or Deceased		Mother Alive or Deceased	
Name		Age	Occupation
Address			
Father Alive or Deceased		Mother Alive or Deceased	
Witnesses			

FAMILY			
NAME	DATE	ADDRESS	FURTHER INFO

NAME

Born	
Address	
Parents (Page)	
Father	
Mother	M.S.
Married	Parish
Died	Age
Address	
Buried	

Census Address	
1841	
1851	
1861	
1871	
1881	
1891	
1901	
1911	

NAME

Born	
Address	
Parents (Page)	
Father	
Mother	M.S.
Married	Parish
Died	Age
Address	
Buried	

Census Address	
1841	
1851	
1861	
1871	
1881	
1891	
1901	
1911	

Married   Address

Name	Age _____ Occupation _____
Address	
Father Alive or Deceased	Mother Alive or Deceased
Name	Age _____ Occupation _____
Address	
Father Alive or Deceased	Mother Alive or Deceased
Witnesses	

FAMILY			
NAME	DATE	ADDRESS	FURTHER INFO

NAME

Born	
Address	

Parents (Page)
Father
Mother   M.S.
Married   Parish

Died _____ Age _____
Address

Buried

Census Address	
1841	
1851	
1861	
1871	
1881	
1891	
1901	
1911	

NAME

Born	
Address	

Parents (Page)
Father
Mother   M.S.
Married   Parish

Died _____ Age _____
Address

Buried

Census Address	
1841	
1851	
1861	
1871	
1881	
1891	
1901	
1911	

Married   Address

Name	Age	Occupation
Address		
Father Alive or Deceased	Mother Alive or Deceased	
Name	Age	Occupation
Address		
Father Alive or Deceased	Mother Alive or Deceased	
Witnesses		

FAMILY			
NAME	DATE	ADDRESS	FURTHER INFO

NAME		NAME	
Born		Born	
Address		Address	
Parents (Page)		Parents (Page)	
Father		Father	
Mother	M.S.	Mother	M.S.
Married	Parish	Married	Parish
Died	Age	Died	Age
Address		Address	
Buried		Buried	

Census Address		Census Address	
1841		1841	
1851		1851	
1861		1861	
1871		1871	
1881		1881	
1891		1891	
1901		1901	
1911		1911	

Married   Address

Name	Age	Occupation
Address		
Father Alive or Deceased	Mother Alive or Deceased	
Name	Age	Occupation
Address		
Father Alive or Deceased	Mother Alive or Deceased	
Witnesses		

FAMILY			
NAME	DATE	ADDRESS	FURTHER INFO

NAME

Born	
Address	

Parents (Page)	
Father	
Mother	M.S.
Married	Parish

Died	Age
Address	
Buried	

NAME

Born	
Address	

Parents (Page)	
Father	
Mother	M.S.
Married	Parish

Died	Age
Address	
Buried	

Census Address
1841
1851
1861
1871
1881
1891
1901
1911

Census Address
1841
1851
1861
1871
1881
1891
1901
1911

Married   Address

Name	Age	Occupation
Address		
Father Alive or Deceased	Mother Alive or Deceased	
Name	Age	Occupation
Address		
Father Alive or Deceased	Mother Alive or Deceased	
Witnesses		

FAMILY			
NAME	DATE	ADDRESS	FURTHER INFO

Contents

and

Certificate Status

B = Birth   M = Marriage   D= Death

Page	Male	Certificates					Female	Relation
No	Name	D	B	M	B	D	Name	
1								G_4
2								G_4
3								G_4
4								G_4
5								G_4
6								G_4
7								G_4
8								G_4
9								G_3
10								G_3
11								G_3
12								G_3
13								G_2
14								G_2
15								G_1
16								G_0
C1	Tree Diagram							
C2	Tree Diagram							
17								G_1
18								G_2
19								G_2
20								G_3
21								G_3
22								G_3
23								G_3
24								G_4
25								G_4
26								G_4
27								G_4
28								G_4
29								G_4
30								G_4
31								G_4

O = Certificate has been obtained.

N = Investigated but certificate not found.

S = Certificate has been sent for.

Blank Space = Investigation has yet to be undertaken.

G_0 = Parents

G_1 = Grand Parents

G_2 = Great Grand Parents

G_3 = Great Great Grand Parents

G_4 = Great Great Great Grand Parents

NOTES

NOTES

NOTES